CLOZE PLUS

CLOZE PLUS

Lynn Hutchinson

HODDER AND STOUGHTON
LONDON   SYDNEY   AUCKLAND   TORONTO

ISBN 0 340 39167 7

First Published 1987
Third Impression 1990

Typeset by Gecko Limited, Bicester, Oxon
Printed in Great Britain for Hodder and Stoughton Educational, a division of
Hodder and Stoughton Ltd, Mill Road, Dunton Green, Sevenoaks, Kent, by
Richard Clay Ltd, Bungay, Suffolk

Contents

1

The Train Journey

Sophie and Ben were on a train. Their toys and games were spread on the table. _____ knocked Ben's game. He was cross. He threw a toy car _____ her. It bounced off the train window.

'Don't _____ that,' said Aunty Lynn. 'The window might _____ .'

Just then there was a bang. Their _____ cracked into a thousand pieces. Ben was upset.

'Will I _____ to pay for it?' he asked.

' _____ ,' said Aunty Lynn. 'That was from outside. It wasn't your _____ .'

A guard passed by. He saw the window.

'You'll have to _____ ,' he said. 'It's not safe.'

'Where _____ ?' asked Aunty Lynn. 'The train is crowded now. _____ are standing!'

'Go to the First Class coaches. There is _____ there.'

They packed up their things. It was a struggle to _____ to the First Class.

The train stopped at the _____ station. The shattered window was knocked _____ . A quick repair was made. It would have to do _____ the end of the journey.

Write the answers to these questions:

1. Who are Sophie and Ben with?
2. Why does Ben throw a toy car?
3. Will Ben have to pay for the window?
4. What does the guard do?
5. Where do they have to go?
6. Why does the train have to stop at the next station?

Think and talk about these questions:

1. Why else shouldn't Ben throw a toy car?
2. Why is Ben upset?
3. What do you think has broken the window?
4. Why do you think it is not safe to stay by the cracked window?
5. In which class coach have they been riding?
6. Why is it a struggle to get to the First Class coach?

2
The Cave

The children ran into the cave.

'Let's hide here,' Dale said. They crouched _____ a boulder.

'What's that?' Dale asked.

'Just scratches,' Kathryn replied. 'No, it's _____ . There are number and letters.' She peered _____ . 'This says *D.H.* Isn't this a number *6*? _____ is a little *f* as well. And _____ arrow and an *N*.'

Dale said, 'Here are some _____ numbers. *One, seven, seven, four.* That's a _____ !'

'Over two hundred years ago! Perhaps *D.H.* was a _____ ! I wonder what *6f* arrow *N* means.'

'An arrow _____ the way,' said Dale. 'I know! Have you looked _____ a map? There is always an arrow _____ *N*. It shows North.'

Kathryn said, 'But there's *6f* first. That might _____ six feet. Perhaps you go six feet north!'

Dale thought. '_____ cave is on the West coast. North _____ be this way.' He took six steps. 'Let's _____ digging!' They scooped sand up with their hands.

'Perhaps it's _____ over. Your feet aren't as big _____ a man's.' They made the hole wider. Then they _____ the chest.

Write the answers to these questions:

1. Why did the children go into the cave?
2. What did the children find on the rock?
3. What date did they find?
4. What does *D.H.* mean?
5. What do they find in the sand?
6. Now draw what the children found on the rock.

Think and talk about these questions:

1. What does *N* mean on the map?
2. Why is *N* shown on a map?
3. How does Dale work out where North is?
4. Why is the chest further away than they think at first?
5. What do you think is in it?
6. How do you think the chest and writing came to be there?

Peacock Feather

The peacock feather lay on the ground. Robert _____ it up.
The colours glowed. As he held _____, Robert started to
shake. He felt air rush past _____. The feeling passed.
Robert looked up. He was in a strange _____! Tall, clipped
hedges were all about him. Was this a maze? Then he
_____ voices.

'The time is ripe,' said a voice. 'I _____ the poison for
the guards.'

'I have waited long for _____ words,' was the reply.
'Tonight, then, the King _____ die!'

Robert was shocked. Where was he? What King was
_____? He heard footsteps. He looked round wildly. He
didn't know _____ way to go! He saw the peacock feather
_____ his feet. He picked it up. The strange shaking came
_____ him again. Then he was back in the zoo gardens.

'I _____ I'll leave that behind!' he thought. He walked
away. The feather _____ on the ground.

Write the answers to these questions:

1. Where was Robert when he first picked up the
   feather?
2. What happened to Robert when he held the feather?
3. What was going to happen to the guards?
4. What was going to happen to the King?
5. What were the men talking about?
6. What did Robert do when he heard footsteps?

Think and talk about these questions:

1. Why did Robert think he was in a maze?
2. Whose voices do you think Robert heard?
3. When do you think he dropped the feather?
4. Why do you think Robert looked round wildly?
5. How did Robert come to be in the maze?
6. Why did he leave the feather behind?

4
The Wall

At the bridge, Susan got off. She propped _____ her bike.
Then she locked it. She set _____. She followed the
footpath for a long time. On the hill _____ was a stile. She
sat on it and looked _____. She was at least three miles
from home. She _____ into the next valley. Her eye _____
a movement. Something red was being waved. What could
it _____? Susan jumped off the stile. She walked _____
the path. Then she heard a shout. It _____ like 'Help!'

    Susan hurried. Beside a broken wall was a boy. Stones
_____ all about.

    'The wall collapsed,' he said.

    'What is the _____?' Susan asked.

    'My leg,' he replied.

    Susan looked. It wasn't the proper _____.

    'I'll go for help,' she said. 'But I'll try to _____ you easy
first.'

    She put the red jersey under _____ head. She put her
jacket round him.

    Then she hurried _____. It was a long way back.

Write the answers to these questions:

1. Where did Susan leave her bike?
2. Did the footpath go up or down from the bridge?
3. How far was the stile from the house?
4. What was it Susan saw in the next valley?
5. Did Susan go up or down the path from the stile to the
   boy?
6. What was the matter with the boy?

Think and talk about these questions:

1. Why did Susan leave her bike at the bridge?
2. Why do you think she locked it?
3. What do you think could have made the wall collapse?
4. How had the boy hurt his leg?
5. Why did Susan make the boy more comfortable?
6. What should Susan do now?

5

Goodbye, Pigeons

The marksman raised his rifle. He took aim. There _____ a dull thud. Then a pigeon dropped _____ the ground. The spotlight moved on. It _____ up a ledge. Some more pigeons could be _____. They were roosting for the night. The _____ shot again. Again a pigeon fell.

This _____ on all night. Five trained marksmen were kept busy. Their _____ had all been silenced. No one was disturbed. The public _____ knew. The marksmen worked from the ground upwards. They picked off the pigeons one _____ one. In the morning there were 300 bodies.

The Town Clerk explained.

'Pigeons _____ a lot of damage. Their droppings eat away the stonework. They _____ the Town Hall look messy. The _____ are a health hazard. We had to _____ something. Gas would have killed other birds. Traps catch very few. _____can't get at the eggs to remove them. This has _____ us £500. We think it is worth it. There seems to be _____ better way.'

Write the answers to these questions:

1. What do you think the spotlight is for?
2. Why aren't people disturbed by the shooting?
3. What damage do pigeons do to a building?
4. What other methods of getting rid of pigeons are thought of?
5. What is the snag about using gas?
6. What is the snag about using traps?

Think and talk about these questions:

1. What makes the dull thud?
2. Why do you think they shoot the pigeons nearest the ground first?
3. If all the marksmen shoot the same number of pigeons, how many do they shoot each?
4. How can pigeons harm people?
5. How would taking eggs solve the pigeon problem?
6. Why are the birds shot at night?

6

The Race

Hari was riding his new bike. Down the street was a dog. It
_____ a small mongrel dog. It was in front _____ a house.
Hari got closer _____ his bike. The dog barked. It ran
towards him. At first Hari thought it _____ to chase him
away. Then he thought it might bite _____ foot. He cycled
faster. He wanted to get _____! The dog ran beside him.
Hari cycled faster still. _____ became a race. The dog ran
along the pavement. Hari cycled _____ the road. They
were both going at speed.

    The dog started _____ edge ahead. Without warning
it swerved _____ the road. Hari tried to miss it. He turned
sharply. The _____ almost jack-knifed. Hari hit the ground.
His hands and knees were grazed. _____ dripped off his
chin on to his shirt. The dog came _____ and licked him. Its
tail was wagging. It had _____ the game. It thought it had
won!

Write the answers to these questions:

1. Where was Hari riding?
2. What did the dog do first?
3. Why did Hari want to get away from the dog?
4. How did Hari try to miss hitting the dog?
5. What happened to the bike when Hari swerved?
6. Why did the dog come up and lick Hari?

Think and talk about these questions:

1. Why do you think the dog started running?
2. What happened to Hari when he swerved on the bike?
3. What injuries do you think Hari had?
4. What is likely to have happened to the bike?
5. Why did the dog think it had won?
6. What would you have done if you had been Hari riding the bike?

7

Owl Care

'Is your owl dead yet?' asked Jamie.

'No,' _____ Anna. 'We think it's going to _____.'

'It seemed very hurt,' Jamie said. 'I didn't _____ it would live.'

'We took it to an owl _____. That's what we call her! She knows all _____ owls. She rescues them. She's got lots of _____ in her garden. They are in cages. The owl lady bathed _____ eye. She says it might stay blind. _____ can't tell yet. We have to make it flap its _____ twice a day. That's so it won't forget _____ to fly. Then she told us how to _____ it.'

'How?' asked Jamie. 'Do you catch mice _____ it?'

'No. We have to use rabbit. We wrap _____ the meat in its skin. One of us holds its beak _____. The other pushes the food right down its _____. Then it gulps it down. The owl lady _____ it might return to the wild. If not, she'll keep _____.'

Write the answers to these questions:

1. What is the matter with the owl?
2. Who has told Anna what to do?
3. Why do they go to see this person?
4. Why do they have to make the owl's wings move?
5. Why do they feed it rabbit?
6. Why are two people needed for feeding?

Think and talk about these questions:

1. Why did Jamie think the owl would be dead?
2. How do you think they make the owl flap its wings?
3. Why can't the owl feed itself?
4. Why do they wrap up the rabbit meat in the skin?
5. What will happen to the owl if its eye doesn't get better?
6. Do you think an owl could live in the wild with one blind eye?

8

The Long Ride

'Here's the camp site.' Laura's father showed them on the _____. 'It's about a hundred miles.'

'Can I cycle?' _____ Laura.

'No,' said her mother. 'It's too far.'

'I suppose she _____ stay at Uncle Peter's. That's thirty miles. Doesn't your friend _____ here?' Mr Sinclair pointed on the map. 'The one _____ moved?'

'Oh, yes!' said Mrs Sinclair.

'Perhaps Laura could stay _____ her. That's forty miles from Uncle Peter's. Then it's only thirty _____ to the camp site. She could do it in three _____.'

'She's far too young! I wouldn't dream _____ letting her go on her _____.'

'You could go with her.'

Mrs Sinclair gasped. 'Me? I _____ got a bike!'

'Let's buy one. We'll look _____ the paper,' was the response.

'But what about luggage? _____ if the bikes go wrong? What _____ Sam?'

'I'll bring Sam in the car. We'll _____ the luggage. We'll get help if you need _____!'

That is almost what happened. But it was the car _____ broke down!

Write the answers to these questions:

1. How far away from home is the camp site?
2. Where could Laura stay the first night?
3. Who lives forty miles from Uncle Peter's?
4. Why won't Mrs Sinclair let Laura go on her own?
5. What do they decide to do about the luggage?
6. What do they decide to do if the bikes go wrong?

Think and talk about these questions:

1. How will they get a bike for Mrs Sinclair?
2. Which day of the journey do you think Laura will most enjoy?
3. Who do you think Sam is?
4. Why do you think Mrs Sinclair agreed to cycle with Laura?
5. What happened to the car?
6. How do you think they got help for the car?

9

Sid's Birthday

It was Sid's birthday. He was eighty. He _____ on his own, now. His cottage was next _____ the Village Hall.

My Mum said we should _____ something. The village should give him a party. People agreed _____ her. They made secret plans.

Some people got the _____ Hall ready. The men put up the trestle _____. Some people cooked party food. My Mum baked a _____ cake.

At four o'clock we were _____. Someone went for Sid. My Mum held the _____. Mrs Wilson started lighting the candles. I had put _____ on. There was one for each year.

The door _____. There stood Sid. We were just _____ to sing. Whoosh! went the candles. There was a huge flame. _____ mother almost dropped the cake. She put it _____ on the nearest table. She and Mrs Wilson _____ madly. They blew it out. The wax had melted all _____ the icing. My mother's eyebrows were singed. But we _____ a lovely party!

Write the answers to these questions:

1. Where did Sid live?
2. Where was the party held?
3. What did the men do towards the party?
4. What else was done towards the party?
5. What did the writer's mother do towards the party?
6. How many candles were on the cake?

Think and talk about these questions:

1. Why did the writer's Mum think the village should do something?
2. Do you think Sid had always lived on his own?
3. Why were the plans secret?
4. Why was there a huge flame?
5. Why do you think the wax melted on the icing?
6. How did the writer's mother get her eyebrows singed?

The Dream

Andrew was tucked up asleep. He was dreaming. He
_____ he was in a palace. He was walking from room to
_____. He was looking for something. He didn't know
_____ it was. He just knew it was somewhere about. He
_____ to some stairs. They swept downwards to the floor
below. Andrew hurried _____ them. He knew he was
getting closer. He went _____ some huge doors. Outside
were stone steps. He could _____ a huge stone vase. It
was at the foot _____ the steps. He knew that what he
wanted was _____ it. He started down the steps. His feet
_____ cold on the stone. He looked down. They _____
quite bare. Then he saw that they weren't on stone. They
were _____ tiles. He looked up. He was in his own
kitchen. _____ mother was holding his arms.

'Wake up,' she _____ gently.

Andrew guessed what had happened.

'Oh bother,' he said. 'Now I'll _____ know what it
was.'

Write the answers to these questions:

1. Where is Andrew when the story starts?
2. Where is Andrew in his dream?
3. What is Andrew doing in the palace?
4. Where do the huge doors lead to?
5. Where is Andrew when he wakes up?
6. How do you think he got there?

Think and talk about these questions:

1. What do you think Andrew is actually doing, when he walks downstairs in his dream?
2. What is in the stone vase?
3. Why do Andrew's feet feel cold in his dream?
4. Why are Andrew's feet really cold?
5. What do you think Andrew's mother is trying to do?
6. What does Andrew mean by the last sentence?

Moped Jousting

Jill and Brian arrived at the field. They had _____ to see the moped jousting. A hundred metres apart _____ two mopeds. Between them was a row _____ straw bales. This made two lanes. There was a moped in _____ lane. The riders put on their helmets. The engines roared. Each _____ had a long stick. On the end was a boxing glove. Then _____ were off! They raced towards each other. Their poles were raised. _____ was laughter as one rider was pushed _____! The winner was cheered. The loser limped off the field. The _____ was picked up.

Someone else wanted to have a _____. He paid his money. He got his helmet and _____ ready. The bikes raced towards each other in first gear. This _____ the first winner wobbled. He reached too far _____ his pole. The bike hit the bales. He _____ off. Jill and Brian laughed.

'This is a good _____ to raise money!' Brian said.

Write the answers to these questions:

1. What did the riders wear to protect themselves?
2. What were the long sticks for?
3. Why did they have boxing gloves on the ends?
4. How long were the lanes?
5. What happened to the first loser?
6. What did you have to do to win?

Think and talk about these questions:

1. What can you tell about the mopeds?
2. What do you think jousting is?
3. What are the bales for?
4. What happens to the winner of each round?
5. What do you have to do if you want a turn at jousting?
6. How does this raise money?

12

Dancing and Playing

Kate lay on her bed. How could _____ choose? Her father was out of work. She had to give _____ one set of lessons. But which should it _____? She loved dancing. She loved playing the flute.

Kate found her wishing _____. This was a piece of quartz. She used to _____ it in her hand and wish. That was when she was _____. It was worth a try now.

'I wish I knew,' she _____.

Later, Kate fell asleep. She had a strange dream. She _____ she was in a room. It contained only a TV _____. On it, a young man was talking to _____ old lady. He said, 'Did you always want to _____ the flute?'

She replied, 'No. I wanted to be a dancer _____ as much. I couldn't do both. I _____ the flute. I don't regret my choice.'

The picture faded. The room _____. Kate woke. 'I wonder if I've _____ my answer,' she thought.

Write the answers to these questions:

1. What did Kate have to choose between?
2. What was her wishing stone?
3. How did she use it?
4. What did she wish for?
5. What else had the old lady wanted to be when she was young?
6. How did the old lady feel about the choice she made?

Think and talk about these questions:

1. Why did Kate have to choose between the lessons?
2. Which lessons did Kate enjoy most?
3. What sort of programme was on the TV?
4. What can you tell about the old lady?
5. Who do you think the old lady could be?
6. What would you choose now if you were Kate? Why?

The Christmas Guinea Pigs

Rudolf and Tinsel were female guinea pigs. They arrived one Christmas morning. Paul chose _____ names.

Rudolf got fatter.

'I think _____ is greedy,' said Paul.

'Perhaps she should run about _____,' said his mother.

'Could she be ill?' asked _____ father.

Paul's mother was worried. She _____ Rudolf to the vet. He looked. He laughed.

'Rudolf _____ soon be a mother! Tinsel must be a male!' _____ was very pleased. Then he was sad. Tinsel _____ have to go. His mother said, 'No _____ babies!'

Paul's friend Matthew wanted Tinsel. He went to _____ with him on his farm.

_____ morning, Paul saw the babies. He couldn't _____ a proper look. He knew he mustn't disturb Rudolf.

_____ day he thought he saw three babies. The _____ after, he had a good look. There _____ four! Paul liked the little brown _____ best. He was pleased when the vet _____ it was female. Now he could _____ Rudolf and Nutty.

Write the answers to these questions:

1. What does Paul think is the matter with Rudolf?
2. Why does Paul's mother take Rudolf to the vet?
3. Why is Rudolf fat?
4. Why can't Paul have a proper look at the babies, at first?
5. Where does Tinsel go?
6. What does Paul call the little brown guinea pig?

Think and talk about these questions:

1. Why do you think Paul chose the names Rudolf and Tinsel?
2. Where do you think the guinea pigs came from?
3. Why does Tinsel have to go?
4. What is good about Tinsel going to Matthew?
5. Why do you think Paul chose the name Nutty?
6. Why can Paul keep Rudolf and Nutty?

The Baby Dragon

Cathy couldn't believe her eyes. She read the headline on the paper again. Yes, she had read it right. She _____ it again. 'Baby Dragon Hatched.' Dragon! But there weren't _____ things! That was what she had been told.

   She looked under the headline. _____ were only a few lines. Cathy struggled _____ read them. She had to find _____! They said the dragon was a rare Komodo dragon. It _____ hatched in a zoo. No one thought the egg would _____. They had had it for years. They _____ it had gone bad. The baby dragon _____ less than 100 grams. Now it was in special care. _____ dragon had ever been born in a zoo before.

   Cathy wondered _____ it looked like. Its wings would _____ tiny. It would be too small to fly. _____ it breathe fire? What did it eat? She _____ she could find out more. She did hope it _____ live.

Write the answers to these questions:

1. What did the headline say?
2. Why was Cathy surprised?
3. What sort of dragon had hatched?
4. Why had they thought the egg was bad?
5. How many dragons had been born in zoos before this one?
6. What did Cathy think the dragon looked like?

Think and talk about these questions:

1. How are baby dragons born?
2. Why do you think it was a struggle for Cathy to read about the dragon?
3. Why was the dragon in special care?
4. How would you look after the baby dragon?
5. How could Cathy find out more about the dragon?
6. Why do you think Cathy wanted the dragon to live?

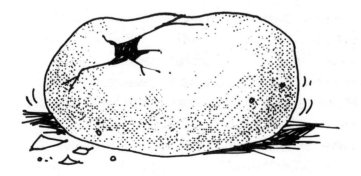

In Disgrace

My cousins are in disgrace. They won't _____ pocket money for years.

It all started last Spring. Martin _____ read all about living rough. He had become very _____. He liked to make fires. Sometimes he cooked food _____ them. Most often it was a tin of beans. _____ didn't seem very rough to me. You wouldn't have _____ of beans in the wild.

Last week it _____ raining. Martin and Wendy were bored. They were _____ up with playing indoors. Wendy's friend was on _____. They couldn't go to Martin's friend. John's mother had _____ he couldn't come round. That was after he'd cut _____ her washing line. He said it was to _____ a ladder.

It was Martin who _____ of the shed. He and Wendy played there for a _____. They made a camp. Then Martin lit a _____ on a tin plate. He thought it would be _____. It might have been, if he hadn't tripped. Sacks _____ fire. Martin and Wendy just got out in _____.

The snag is, sheds cost a lot of _____.

Write the answers to these questions:

1. What was Martin keen on?
2. What are Martin and Wendy being punished for?
3. Why couldn't Martin go to John's house?
4. What did Martin want the washing line for?
5. Why couldn't they go to Wendy's friend's house?
6. How did the fire spread?

Think and talk about these questions:

1. How are Martin and Wendy being punished?
2. How would you cook beans on a camp fire?
3. Why do you think John's mother didn't want Martin around?
4. What sort of things are kept in garden sheds?
5. What do you think this shed was probably made of?
6. How might this story have ended?

Strange Pets

It was nearly Sharmila's birthday. She wanted a tarantula.

'They don't all poison people,' she _____.

'No,' said her mother. 'I hate spiders. I'll hoover it _____!'

'No,' said her father. 'The cat _____ eat it. I might step on it!'

'All right. _____ I have a lizard?' Sharmila asked.

Her parents thought.

'_____,' said her father. 'But you must find _____ about them first.'

Sharmila dashed to the library. She _____ four books on reptiles.

Sharmila's father _____ her to the pet shop. The owner _____ Sharmila some questions.

'I only let my pets _____ to good homes,' he said. 'I think you will _____ after them.'

Sharmila chose two lizards. _____was a Blue. The other was _____ Asian Anolis. She also chose a heated tank. _____ home, she held the lizards.

'Hello Wembley. Hello Mokey. _____ smooth, soft skins you have!'

She put them in the _____. She put in some live crickets. For tea they would _____ live meal worms.

Write the answers to these questions:

1. What is a tarantula?
2. Who doesn't want a tarantula?
3. What does Sharmila keep the lizards in?
4. What do lizards eat?
5. What do lizards' skins feel like?
6. What does Sharmila call the lizards?

Think and talk about these questions:

1. What might happen to a tarantula in Sharmila's house?
2. Why does Sharmila's father say Sharmila must find out about lizards first?
3. Why does Sharmila borrow books on reptiles?
4. Why does the pet shop owner ask Sharmila questions?
5. Why do you think Sharmila's father buys the lizards and tank for her?
6. Why do you think the tank is heated?

Whoops!

First came the check. Brakes, tyres, cranks and headsets
_____ approved.

'Riders ready, pedals ready, go!'

The starting gate slammed down. All the _____ sped
down the ramp. They gathered _____. In no time they
were on the first camel back. Robin _____ on tightly. His
bike went up, then _____. He stayed on. He rode hard into
the berm. This was _____ the track went round a bend. It
curved upwards into a wall. Robin _____ hard round the
bend. He used to fall _____ just here. That was when he
first started _____. Now, he stayed on. The track
straightened. He rode _____ a large camel back. Then
came a whoops. This was _____ a double camel back. It
had two _____. Robin felt pleased. He was in third _____.
Then someone rode into him. It was the _____ of the race
for both of them.

Write the answers to these questions:

1. What is Robin riding?
2. Which parts of it are checked?
3. What is a camel back?
4. What is a berm?
5. What is a whoops?
6. What happens to Robin at the end?

Think and talk about these questions:

1. Which two things at the beginning tell you the story is about a race?
2. Why do you think the bikes were checked?
3. Why is the track curved at the bend?
4. Why do you think Robin used to fall off at the first berm?
5. Why do you think he can stay on at the berm now?
6. Why do you think someone rode into him?

18
Country Ways

Sally and Tom wanted to explore.

'Stick to the paths,' _____ their aunt. 'Always close gates.' She knew they weren't _____ to country ways.

They went up the hill. Then they _____ the stile. Some cattle were gathered at the other top corner of the _____. The path ran down the field to the river. They took _____ their shoes and socks and paddled.

Later, as they walked up the field, the _____ moved down it. Soon the path _____ blocked. They all stopped.

'Are they bulls?' asked _____.

'I don't know,' said Tom. He stepped forward. One _____ the beasts put its head down. He stepped back. 'Let's _____ over that fence,' he said. 'I think there's a path.'

They moved slowly _____ the edge of the field. The cattle followed slowly. Quickly they climbed _____ the fence.

'Oh no!' Sally exclaimed.

Tom looked. The _____ ahead was overgrown with waist-high nettles. There was _____ other way round. He looked back. The cattle _____ pushing round the fence.

Write the answers to these questions:

1. Where do you think Sally and Tom live?
2. Why does their aunt tell them what to do?
3. What did they do in the river?
4. Why can't they go back the way they came?
5. Which way does Tom suggest going back?
6. Why does Sally say 'Oh no!'?

Think and talk about these questions:

1. What do you think Sally and Tom were doing in the country?
2. What clothes do you think they would be wearing?
3. Why do you think the cattle show such interest in Tom and Sally?
4. Why does Tom suggest going over the fence?
5. What possible courses of action do Tom and Sally have?
6. What would you do?

19

The Gala

It was the day of the Gala. Swimmers _____ many clubs were there. It was the first _____ Hannah had swum for Bridgelea. She did _____ to do her best. This was _____ big chance.

'Isn't Sharon with your team?' a girl _____. 'No,' answered Hannah. 'She's ill.'

'Oh!' came the _____. 'That gives us a chance then!'

Hannah saw the _____ go off to tell the others. They all _____ pleased. They had good reason. Sharon was _____ known. She won most of her races. The relay team _____ well when she swam with them.

For this Gala, Jenny _____ taking Sharon's place. Hannah was taking Jenny's place _____ the relay race. She looked at the board. Bridgelea _____ third. Then came the result of the boy's relay _____. Bridgelea moved up to second place.

Hannah took her _____ at the poolside.

A few minutes later it was _____. The Bridgelea team was still second.

Write the answers to these questions:

1. Which club did Hannah belong to?
2. Why was this Hannah's big chance?
3. Why wasn't Sharon there?
4. Whose place was Hannah taking in the relay race?
5. Who was taking Sharon's place in the other races?
6. What position was Bridgelea in after the girls' relay race?

Think and talk about these questions:

1. What is a Gala?
2. Why were the other girls pleased Sharon wasn't there?
3. Where do you think Jenny was in the relay race?
4. Why was Hannah swimming in the relay race?
5. How do you think the Birdgelea boys did in their relay race?
6. Do you think the Bridgelea girls finished first, second or third in their relay race?

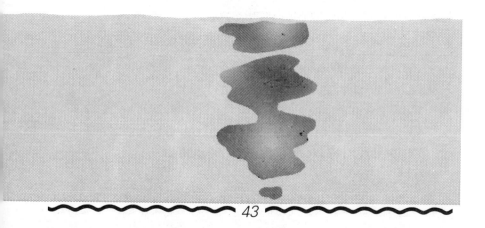

Chicken and Eggs

'Can I get the eggs?' asked Matthew.

'Yes, _____ you are careful,' replied his Mum.

'Don't let any chickens _____ out,' warned his Dad.
'I don't want _____ on the young plants.'

Matthew was careful. He _____ into the chicken run.
He closed the door behind _____. He looked in the nest
boxes. He found only two _____. He carried them to the
door of the run. He _____ the eggs down to open it. As he
_____ it, a chicken ran out. It ran into his father's garden.
Matthew _____ after it. He chased it over the peas. He
followed _____ through the beans. It squawked as
Matthew grabbed it.

His _____ heard the noise. They ran out.

'Matthew!' shouted his _____. 'What have you done
to my plants?'

Matthew looked _____ the trodden garden. Then he
looked at where he'd put the eggs. The _____ were eating
them.

'Oh Matthew!' said his mother. 'Now they've tasted
eggs they'll eat _____ own.'

Write the answers to these questions:

1. What did Matthew's Dad tell him to do?
2. Where did Matthew find the eggs?
3. How did the chicken get out of the run?
4. Why did Matthew's parents run out?
5. What do you think Matthew had done to the plants?
6. What did the chickens do to the eggs?

Think and talk about these questions:

1. Why did Matthew's Mum tell him to be careful?
2. Why didn't Matthew's Dad want the chickens out?
3. Why did Matthew put the eggs on the ground?
4. Why did Matthew tread on the plants?
5. What will chickens do once they have tasted eggs?
6. What will this mean for the family?

21

First Morning

Polly woke early. The sun was streaming through the
_____. The room was warm and stuffy. She looked at the
_____. It was five thirty. How could she lie awake _____
hours? The others would sleep for ages.

'I'm getting _____,' she thought. 'I can't waste this
first lovely day.' _____ got dressed. She went out to
explore. Outside the cottage the _____ was wet with dew.
On it _____ lots of black slugs! The air smelt of wet earth.
Scent _____ the roses drifted towards her. She looked
_____ the remote valley. Only the sheep moved. The next
_____ was a mile away. Between the cottages there
_____ a river and fields. _____ home, the same distance
was covered with houses. There, _____ would be on the
roads by now. Cars were always about. Instead of city
_____ she could hear bees and grasshoppers. The river
murmured. Home _____ years away.

Write the answers to these questions:

1. What time did Polly wake?
2. Why did Polly want to get up?
3. What was on the wet grass?
4. What could Polly hear?
6. How long had she been at the cottage?

Think and talk about these questions:

1. Why do you think Polly woke so early?
2. What can you tell about where the cottage was?
3. Had Polly been there before? How do you know?
4. What was land used for at home?
5. What was land used for round the cottage?
6. What do you think Polly was doing at the cottage?

22

In the Boot

'Look what Simon's got!' Carol and Tim stopped. They
_____ up their bikes. Lucy was holding up a Wellington
_____. They looked over the gate.

'Look! In the boot!' Lucy _____ it closer. Carol and
Tim looked inside. There _____ a sudden hiss. A green
head reared towards _____! Startled, they leapt
backwards.

'What is _____?' Carol asked.

'A grass snake,' Simon _____.

'Can it hurt?' Tim asked.

'We don't think _____,' said Lucy. The snake was
waving its head _____.

'What's it doing in your boot?' asked Carol.

_____ replied, 'I was going down Snakes Lane. There
was this _____ on the track. It was basking in the sun. I
_____ to bring it home. It seemed the safest way to
_____ it.'

'So that's why it's called Snakes _____!' Tim said.

'What are you going to _____ now?' asked Carol.

'I want to keep it. Just _____ a few days. But I've got
to _____ out how!'

Write the answers to these questions:

1. What has Simon caught?
2. What did he catch it in?
3. Where did he find it?
4. Why are Carol and Tim startled?
5. Why didn't Simon leave it where it was?
6. What is he going to do with it?

Think and talk about these questions:

1. What were Carol and Tim doing when Lucy called?
2. Why do you think the snake reared up?
3. Why does Tim ask if it can hurt?
4. Why do you think the track is called Snakes Lane?
5. How do you think Simon got home?
6. How will they find out how to keep it?

23

The Shed

The shed at the end of the garden _____ full. There were boxes in it. There _____ bikes, buckets and balls. The lawn mower stayed _____. So did all the garden tools.

    The Gibsons were moving _____. Mr Gibson made _____ his mind. It was a nice Spring day. He would clear out the _____. Kevin and Clare helped. They put the things _____ the grass.

    After a while, Clare reached her mother's old _____. In the basket was a nest. In the nest were four baby _____. They had huge beaks and fine grey fluff for feathers.

    'We'll _____ to stop,' Clare whispered. 'We'll have to wait _____ they can fly.'

    They went out of the shed. A robin _____ past. It settled on a branch nearby. A second _____ landed on the branch.

    Kevin said, 'Those must be the _____. They are waiting for us to go away. They won't fly in _____ we are here.'

Write the answers to these questions:

1. What was kept in the shed?
2. Why did Mr Gibson need to clear it out?
3. Why did he choose this day?
4. What time of year was it?
5. What was in the basket?
6. What will the baby birds look like when they are adult?

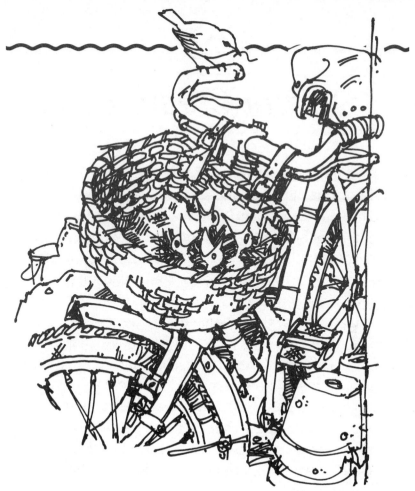

Think and talk about these questions:

1. What is good and bad about the place the robins have chosen to build their nest?
2. What might happen if the Gibsons carry on clearing out the shed?
3. Why is it all right to clear the shed after the birds can fly?
4. Why are the robins waiting for the people to go away?
5. Why won't they fly into the shed while someone is there?
6. What do you think the Gibsons will have to do now about the things in the shed?

24

Water Creatures

In Philip's net there was a small dark insect. It _____ long, thick front legs. It moved _____ like oars.

'That's a water boatman,' Dinah said. The next sweep _____ the net brought two shrimps. They were _____ in the bucket with the water boatman. _____ this time the water was _____ muddy. The children found lots of tiny creatures. They found _____ later what they were. They _____ water fleas. Then a large black insect was _____. Its front legs were very big and strong. They _____ a bit like a crab's pincers. It had a long, sharp tail _____ a sword.

'What's that?' Mark asked. 'It looks fierce!'

Dinah said, '_____ is! That's a water scorpion. I've seen pictures of _____. That isn't a proper tail. It's a breathing tube. Look, you can _____ a bubble of air!'

'One of my _____ has gone,' Philip said. 'There were two of them with the _____ boatman.'

Write the answers to these questions:

1. How do the children catch the creatures?
2. Where are the creatures kept?
3. How does the water scorpion breathe?
4. Which is the biggest creature found?
5. Which is the smallest creature found?
6. How many types of creature do they find?

Think and talk about these questions:

1. Where do these creatures live?
2. How do you think the water boatman got its name?
3. How do you think the children found out what the water fleas were?
4. Why do you think the water gets muddy?
5. What two things make the water scorpion look fierce?
6. Where do you think the shrimp has gone?

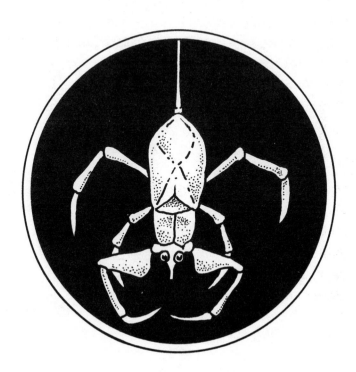

25
Channel Crossing

Barry peered into the fog.

'I can't see a thing,' he _____.

'There's nothing there to see,' Patrick replied. 'We are out of _____ of land.'

'Come on, you boys,' called their teacher. '_____ inside the cabin where I can see you. I don't _____ you falling overboard!'

Patrick gave a last _____ at the sea.

'Barry!' He pointed into the fog. 'I can _____ something!'

Mr White was getting annoyed.

'Now!' he called.

'We can see _____!' Patrick called back. 'Come and see!'

Mr White made his way _____ them.

'You'd better not be fooling!' he warned. He looked _____ Barry pointed.

'You're right! It looks _____ a small boat! Stay here and I'll _____ someone!'

The engines reversed, then stopped. A small motor _____ was launched. In minutes four men were _____. They were soon aboard the ferry.

In assembly, the story was _____. Mr White held up the local paper. The _____ read: Coaster Sinks in Channel. Boys Spot Drifting Crew.

Write the answers to these questions:

1. Why can't Barry see anything?
2. What are the boys travelling on?
3. Who is Mr White?
4. Why does he want them in the cabin?
5. Who spots the small boat?
6. How are the men reached?

Think and talk about these questions:

1. What do you think the boys are doing on the ferry?
2. Why would rescue have been difficult if a boy had fallen overboard?
3. Why do you think the engines go into reverse before they stop?
4. In what two ways do the others at school find out about the rescue?
5. Where have the four men come from?
6. How do you think they came to be in the boat?

Woolly Bear

'Don't touch that one,' Michael said.

'What is _____?' asked Jayne.

'A woolly bear,' laughed Michael.

'No, it's _____. It's a caterpillar. Why can't I _____ it?' Michael said, 'The hairs are itchy. You might _____ a rash on your skin. That's how it protects itself. _____ birds will eat it, except the cuckoo.'

They looked _____ the hairy creature. It was eating dock leaves.

'_____ will it turn into?' Jayne asked.

'A garden tiger moth,' Michael _____.

'Will birds eat it then?' Jayne asked.

'No,' said _____. 'It is poisonous to a bird.'

'That's not fair on the _____!' said Jayne.

'Well, the birds are warned,' Michael said. 'It _____ very bright hind wings. They are red and black. Brightly _____ moths often have a nasty taste. Birds know that. The _____ tiger moth also has a fringe of red hairs behind _____ neck. It raises these up if it is _____. The bird soon gets the message.'

Write the answers to these questions:

1. What is a woolly bear?
2. What will the woolly bear grow into?
3. Which bird eats woolly bears?
4. Why don't other birds eat woolly bears?
5. What might happen if Jayne touches the woolly bear?
6. What do woolly bears eat?

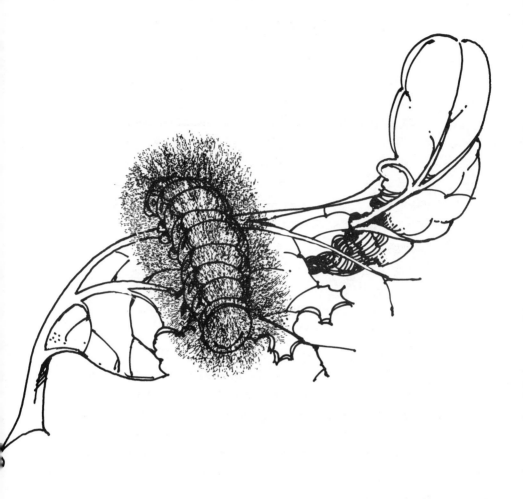

Think and talk about these questions:

1. How do you think the woolly bear got its name?
2. Why won't birds eat garden tiger moths?
3. You know the hind wings are red and black. What do you think the fore wings look like?
4. What do you think Jayne means about it not being fair on the bird?
5. How do birds know which moths to eat?
6. How does the garden tiger moth frighten birds away?

27

A Real Pet

Ruth's Dad loved dogs. He liked large dogs best, _____ the family lived in a block _____ flats. This meant they couldn't keep a _____. Ruth's Mum came home with a kitten one _____. Ruth was very pleased. Ruth's Dad teased her.

'You can't call that a pet,' he _____. 'It's too small. A real pet would _____ it for breakfast! So it must be some use. What?'

'It _____ keep the mice away,' Ruth said.

'We haven't _____ any,' her Dad replied. 'Do you think it _____ frighten a burglar? That would be a very useful thing to _____.'

'It would miaow. That would wake us up.'

'Of course _____ would,' agreed her Dad. 'Then we would all jump _____ of bed. I could shout, "Get them, Fang!" They _____ run away. What a relief! Our money is _____ now we have a kitten to protect us!'

_____ was how Fang came to live with _____.

Now write the answers to these sentences:

1. Can you name the sort of dogs Ruth's Dad likes best?
2. Why can't they keep a dog?
3. Why does Ruth's Dad think the kitten isn't a real pet?
4. Why can't the kitten catch mice?
5. How would the kitten tell them of burglars?
6. What is the kitten's name?

Think and talk about these questions:

1. Why does Ruth's Dad think the kitten must have a use?
2. What does Ruth's Dad think would be a useful thing for a pet to do?
3. Do you think a kitten would wake them all up?
4. Why would Ruth's Dad shout, 'Get them, Fang!'?
5. Why would the burglars run away when Ruth's Dad shouted?
6. Why do you think the kitten was called Fang?

28

Saving the Barley

We live in a small village. It is _____ a country called
Ghana. Near us is a place _____ beer is made. A lot of
barley is _____ in this brewery. The used barley was
dumped. One hundred tons a week _____ thrown away.

My father thought this was a _____. He wondered if it
could be saved. There was still goodness in _____. The
snag was that the _____ was wet. In one day, it started to
go bad. The problem was _____ to get the water out
quickly.

Visitors came to our village. _____ offered to help
with our work problems. My father _____ them about this
barley. They thought about it. They _____ drawings. Then
they made a press for us. It could _____ turned by hand. A
lot of the water was pressed _____. Then the barley
finished drying in the sun.

_____ father now sells this barley. It is used _____
cattle food.

Write the answers to these questions:

1. Which country is this village in?
2. Where is the beer made?
3. What used to happen to the used barley?
4. Why was the barley thrown away?
5. How do they now get the water out of the barley?
6. What is the barley used for now?

Think and talk about these questions:

1. Who buys the dried barley?
2. What sort of weather do you think there is in Ghana?
3. What was wasteful about throwing out the barley?
4. How did the visitors help to solve the problem?
5. Why do you think they helped?
6. How is the village better off since the visitors came?